Monkeys

Monkeys	2
Story: Little Monkey and the Sun	9
Rhyme: There is a Monkey	20
Activities	21
Picture Dictionary	23

Written by Joanna Pascoe
Illustrated by Fran &
David Brylewska

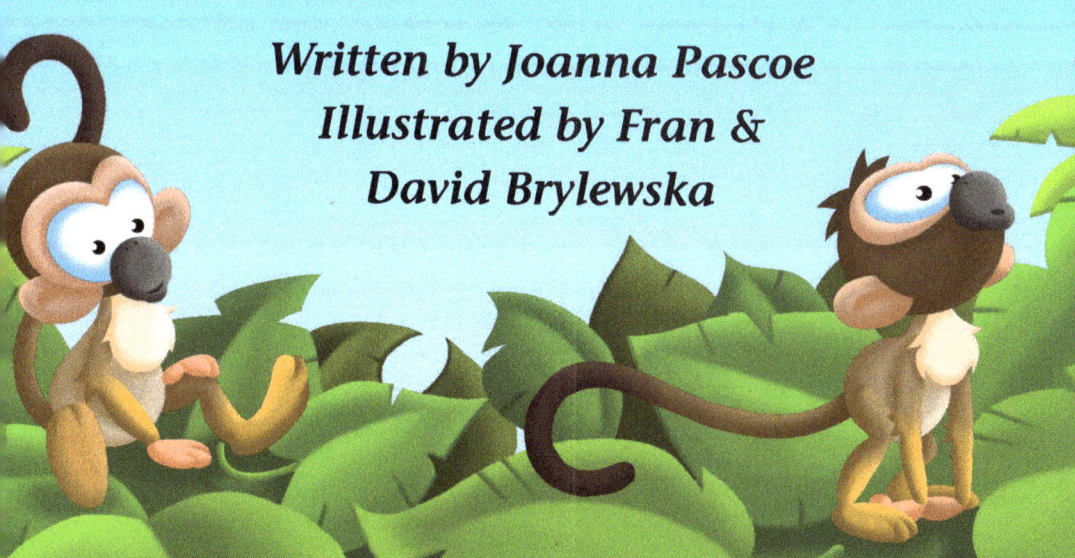

Where monkeys live

Many monkeys live in rainforests. They live in the trees.

Monkeys live in big families.

What monkeys eat

Monkeys like to eat fruit, nuts and eggs. They use their hands to eat.

What monkeys look like

Monkeys have got long legs and arms.

Tail

Arm

Leg

Hand

They have got a long tail to hold on to branches.

Japanese snow monkeys

Snow monkeys live in Japan. They have got very thick fur.

Amazing Fact
In winter, snow monkeys sit in hot pools to keep warm.

Squirrel monkeys

Squirrel monkeys live in Central and South America.

They jump through the trees like squirrels.

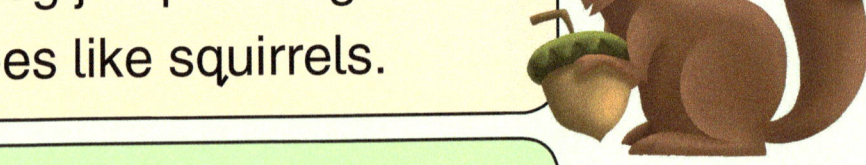

He's not like me at all!

Amazing Fact
Squirrel monkeys are noisy. They make sounds like dogs.

Golden lion tamarins

Golden lion tamarins live in Brazil.

He's not like me at all!

They have got golden manes like lions.

Baboons

Baboons are big monkeys. They have got very big teeth!

Amazing Fact
Baboons can learn to read words.

Let's read a story about a little monkey.

Little Monkey and the Sun

Written by Joanna Pascoe
Illustrated by Fran & David Brylewska

Paz is a little squirrel monkey. He lives with his mother in the rainforest.

Then Paz sees the sun.

Look! It is yellow and orange and red.

Suddenly, the sun shines on the top of the tree.

What's that? It's yellow and it smells good to eat.

There is a Monkey

There is a monkey in a tree.
A little squirrel monkey.
What does he see?

He can see some fruit for lunch.
Look, bananas.
There's a whole bunch!

Activities

1 Colour and label the fruit.

2 Complete the sentences.

> jump on a trampoline   climb a tree   ~~fly with a kite~~

1 Paz can <u>fly with a kite</u>.

2 Paz can _____ _____.

3 Paz can _____ _____.

Picture Dictionary

tree　　rainforest　　branch　　pool

fur　　squirrel　　jump　　lion's mane

teeth　　hungry　　breakfast　　sun

trampoline　　kite　　climb　　smell

Macmillan Education
4 Crinan Street
London N1 9XW
A division of Springer Nature Limited
Companies and representatives throughout the world

ISBN 978-0-230-44367-9

Text, design and illustration © Springer Nature Limited 2013
Written by Joanna Pascoe
The author has asserted her right to be identified as the author of this work in accordance with the Copyright, Design and Patents Act 1988.

First published 2013

All rights reserved; no part of this publication may be reproduced, stored in a retrieval system, transmitted in any form, or by any means, electronic, mechanical, photocopying, recording, or otherwise, without the prior written permission of the publishers.

Designed by Carolyn Gibson
Illustrated by Fran & David Brylewska
Picture research by Victoria Gaunt
Cover photograph by FLPA/Imagebroker

The author and publishers would like to thank the following for permission to reproduce their photographs:
Corbis/Lars-Olof Johansson/Johnér Images p6; **FLPA**/IMAGEBROKER/CHRISTIAN HüTTER p8, FLPA/Jurgen & Christine Sohns pp2, 4; **Getty Images**/Russell Sadur p3(fruit), Getty Images/Lucia Terui p5; **Rex Features**/Jeremy Durkin p7; **Superstock**/Imagebroker.net p3(monkey).

These materials may contain links for third party websites. We have no control over, and are not responsible for, the contents of such third party websites. Please use care when accessing them.

Although we have tried to trace and contact copyright holders before publication, in some cases this has not been possible. If contacted we will be pleased to rectify any errors or omissions at the earliest opportunity.

Printed and bound in Great Britain by Ashford Colour Press Ltd

2019
10 9 8 7 6